Treasure Island

Written by Lisa Thompson

Pictures by Craig Smith

The ship was going
to Treasure Island.

"Are you going to Treasure Island?" said the mermaids.

"Go that way."

"We are going to Treasure Island," said the dolphins.

"Come this way."

"We will help you to
go fast," said the winds.

The ship went on and on.

"That is Treasure Island,"
said the birds.

"And this is the treasure!" said the pirates.

"Hurray!"

Think About!
How many different creatures and things helped the pirates?
What is the monkey doing at the end of the story?
What do you think the pirates will do with their treasure?